PETS OWNER

Name : ....

Adresse : ....

....

Phone Number : ....

Email : ....

THIS HEALTH RECORD AND JOURNAL BOOK BELONG TO:

....

....

Pet Informations 1

Name :

Date of Birth :

Adoption day :

Gender :

Breed :

Coat color :

Eye Color :

PICTURE

Identification

Microship: Registry :

Spicial markings :

Medical

Neutered : Yes ◯ No ◯ Date of neutered : / /

Allergies :

Medical conditions :

Vet information

Clinic : Vet :

Phone : Email : @

Adresse :

Owner's Information

Owner's Name : Phone :

Adresse :

Pet Informations 2

Name : ....

Date of Birth : ....

Adoption day : ....

Gender : ....

Breed : ....

Coat color : ....

Eye Color : ....

PICTURE

Identification

Microship: .... Registry : ....

Spicial markings : ....

Medical

Neutered : Yes ○ No ○ Date of neutered : ..../..../....

Allergies : ....

Medical conditions : ....

....

Vet information

Clinic : .... Vet : ....

Phone : .... Email : ....@..............

Adresse : ....

Owner's Information

Owner's Name : .... Phone : ....

Adresse : ....

Pet Health Record 1

Vaccinations	Date	Description

Pet Health Record 1

Vaccinations	Date	Description

Pet Health Record 2

Vaccinations	Date	Description

Pet Health Record 2

Vaccinations	Date	Description

Pet Health Record 1

Labwork	Date	Description

Pet Health Record 1

Labwork	Date	Description

Pet Health Record 2

Labwork	Date	Description

Pet Health Record 2

Labwork	Date	Description

Pet Health Record 1

Surgery	Date	Description

Pet Health Record 2

Surgery	Date	Description

Pet Contact 1

Name/company	Phone	Adresse	E-mail

Pet Contact 1

Name/company	Phone	Adresse	E-mail

Pet Contact 2

Name/company	Phone	Adresse	E-mail

Pet Contact 2

Name/company	Phone	Adresse	E-mail

Pet Appointment

Name/company	Phone	Appointment	E-mail

Pet Appointment

Name/company	Phone	Appointment	E-mail

Pet Appointment

Name/company	Phone	Appointment	E-mail

Pet Appointment

Name/company	Phone	Appointment	E-mail

Pet Appointment

Name/company	Phone	Appointment	E-mail

Pet Appointment

Name/company	Phone	Appointment	E-mail

Pet Appointment

Name/company	Phone	Appointment	E-mail

Pet Appointment

Name/company	Phone	Appointment	E-mail

Pet Appointment

Name/company	Phone	Appointment	E-mail

Pet Appointment

Name/company	Phone	Appointment	E-mail

Pets Journal

Made in the USA
Middletown, DE
26 April 2022